Can You Guess?
(Animals of Thailand)

I live in the jungle far, far away,
Where I eat bananas every day.

My body is hairy and coloured brown,
And I love to hang upside down.

I have a long curly tail, I've legs and arms too,
And fingers and toes, just like you.

I swing through the air from tree to tree,

Can you guess?

I'm a ....

2

My skin is wrinkled and coloured grey,
And when I walk my body sways.

I have two floppy ears and a long curly
nose,
That squirts out water like a hose.

My body is huge ... as large as a house!
But I can be scared by a tiny mouse.

I can paint, kick a ball, and do other stunts,

Can you guess?

I'm an ....

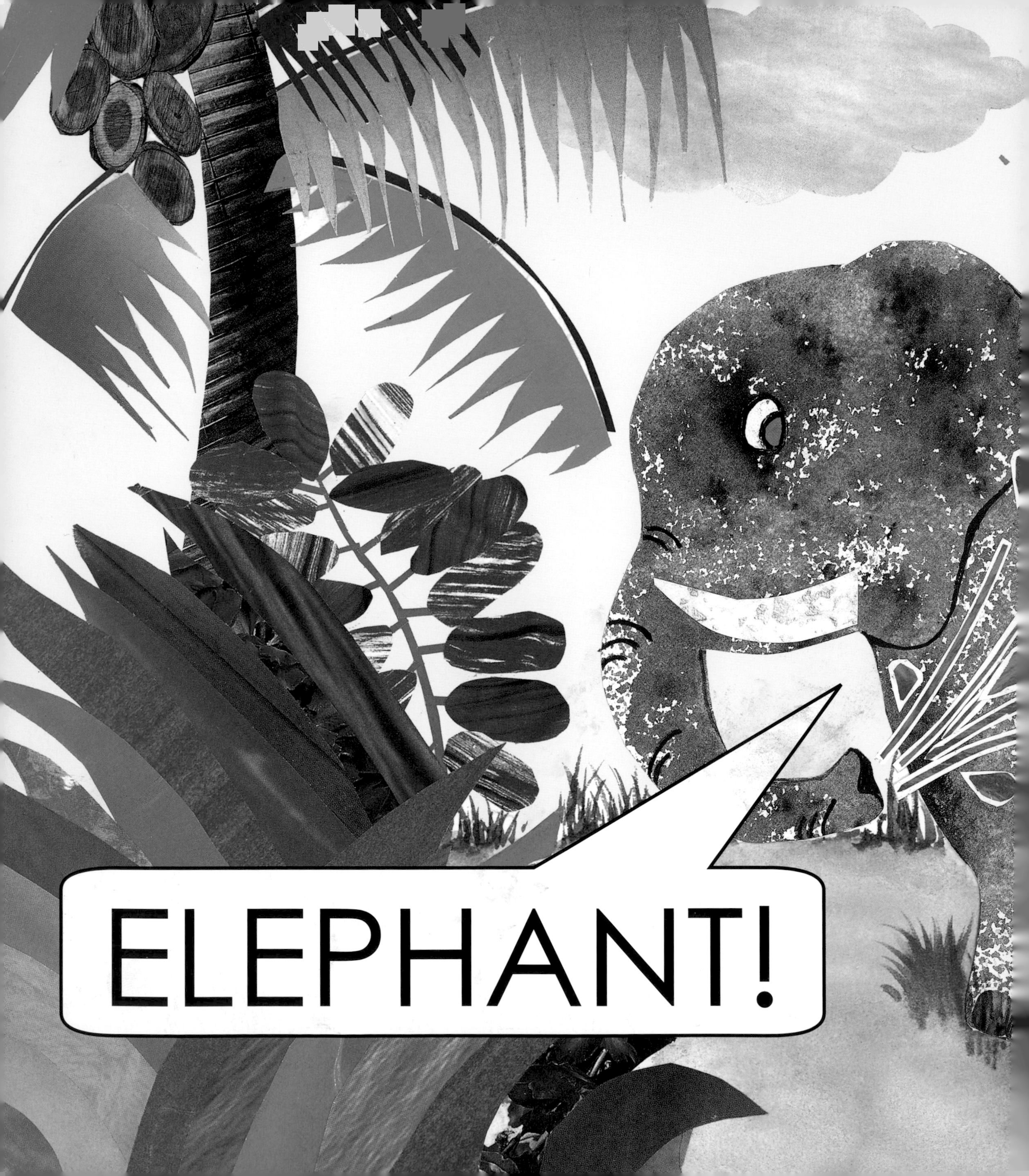
ELEPHANT!

I'm long and thin from head to tail,
And my body is covered with slimy scales.

I have no legs, but I'm not slow,
For I just wriggle where I want to go.

My face puffs up when I get scared,
And if I bite, you'll soon be dead.

I love to lie in the sun and bake,

Can you guess?

I'm a ....

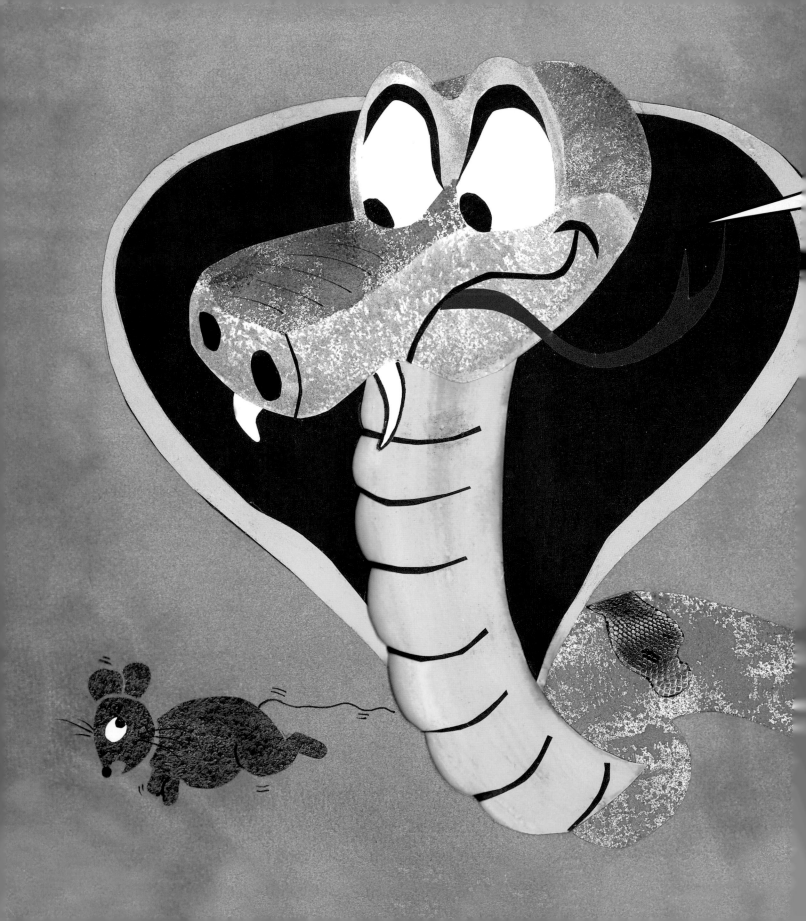

I'm brown on my face and brown on my
back,
But the tips of my ears and paws are black.

My eyes are blue; I have soft silky fur,
And when you pat me I go "purrrrr".

I lap up milk and I chew on fish,
You feed me in my own special dish.

I like to chase big hairy rats,

Can you guess?

I'm a ....

I've two long horns; I'm greyish-brown,
And I live on a farm, far from town.

I work in the rice fields every day,
And like to chew on grass and hay.

When it's hot and I want to stay cool,
I plop myself down in a muddy pool.

I pull a plough to and fro,

Can you guess?

I'm a ....

I have a long green nose and a long green tail,
And my body is covered with pointy scales.

I lie in the sun at the river shore,
With my big sharp teeth and four sharp claws.

I sit very still with my mouth open wide,
Waiting for some food to step inside.

Oooh, I'd like to taste a juicy child,

Can you guess?

I'm a ....

I have four legs and a tail; I'm yellowish-
brown,
And walk through the sois in your town.

I have no home; I just roam the streets,
Looking for crunchy bones to eat.

You might hear me howl and bark,
When I pass by your house after dark.

I nip at your heels when you jog,

Can you guess?

I'm a ....

I've a tiny body, smaller than a mouse,
And you can find me inside your house.

I have a long tail and four sticky feet,
And insects are what I like to eat.

I can sometimes hear you squealing,
When you see me running on your ceiling.

I'm coloured brown from head to toe,

Can you guess?

I'm a ....

I have tough green skin, my eyes are black,
I have four short legs and a shell on my
back.

I crawl very slowly when I am on land,
And I lay my eggs in a hole in the sand.

If I am caught in a fisherman's net,
I'm put in a pond and kept as a pet.

I'm old and slow; I can't run or hurdle,

Can you guess?

I'm a ....

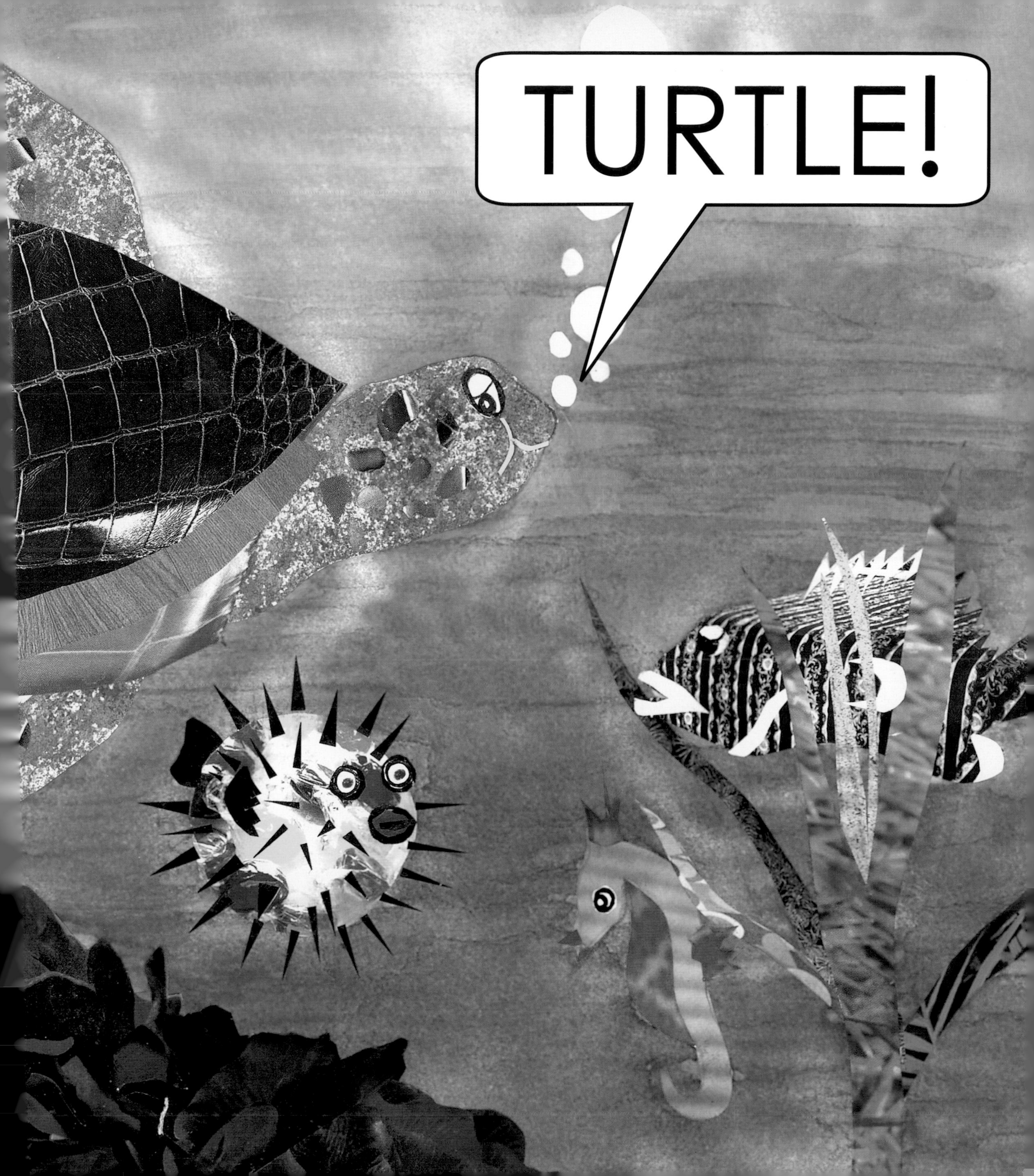
TURTLE!

I love to swim but I can't go far,
Because I live inside a jar.

My body's pretty; I'm red and white,
But my owners keep me out of sight,

No one dares come close to me,
Because I bite anyone I see.

I have long fins and my tail goes swish,

Can you guess?

I'm a ....

FIGHTING

Meet the Author

Janice is an Australian who has lived in Bangkok for almost 20 years. She is married and has three children. She is a graduate of the University of Melbourne and has a Math/Science teaching degree as well as a PhD in Chemistry. Before coming to Thailand she worked as a Research Scientist in the USA. After settling down in Bangkok, she taught English at a Thai school for several years before publishing her first book, The Little Blue Tuk-tuk, in 2000. She is now a full-time writer.

Other books by the same author

The Little Blue Tuk-tuk by Janice Santikarn, illustrated by Sukit Tanmankong, Thai Watana Panich Press, Bangkok, 2000. Reprinted Sirivatana Interprint Public Co. Ltd., Bangkok, 2006

Nawin Saves the Elephants by Janice Santikarn, illustrated by Rong Prapasanobon, Thai Watana Panich Press, Bangkok, 2000

ABC of Thailand by Janice Santikarn, illustrated by Janice Santikarn and Toni Skinner, Rung Silp Printing, Bangkok, 2001. Reprinted Sirivatana Interprint Public Co. Ltd., Bangkok, 2003

Koko the Monkey: Lost in Bangkok by Janice Santikarn, illustrated by Prateep Paisarnnan, Sirivatana Interprint Public Co. Ltd., Bangkok, 2002. Reprinted 2005

When I Grow Up (In Thailand) by Janice Santikarn, illustrated by Sasawat Kayaroj, Sirivatana Interprint Public Co. Ltd., Bangkok, 2003. Reprinted 2006

The Brave Little Tuk-tuk by Janice Santikarn, illustrated by Sukit Tanmankong, Sirivatana Interprint Public Co. Ltd., Bangkok, 2004